Kodály, Zoltán

KODÁLY
CHORAL METHOD

66

TWO-PART
EXERCISES

Edited with annotations by

Percy M. Young

University of Tulsa
McFarlin Library
Tulsa, Oklahoma

Boosey & Ha
Music Publishers
London · Paris · Bonn · Johannesburg · Sydn... New York

D1225719

Editor's Introduction

This volume of sight-reading exercises in two parts was first issued in Budapest in 1962, since when it has been extensively and profitably used in the schools of Hungary. In relation to the other volumes of the *Choral Method* already available in the English edition it is suggested that this collection should be taken to constitute a bridge between *333 Elementary Exercises* (unison) and *Bicinia Hungarica, I* (2-part songs). There is, of course, no reason why these exercises should not be undertaken concurrently with items from the books named. There is, in fact, much to be said in favour of beginning sight-reading in two parts when two thirds of the way through *333 Exercises*, since the first section of the present series is based on melodies of comparable standard of ease—or difficulty—in execution.

There are good reasons for starting sight-reading in two parts as soon as possible. This should be when pupils have gained some facility in singing a single melodic line at sight, and in any case not later than the beginning of the secondary school course. The advantages may be enumerated as follows:

(1) A greater independence in singing is established through the need to concentrate on the presentation of one part against another.

(2) Intonation and rhythm become more accurate when it is understood that miscalculations in these particulars destroy musical coherence.

(3) Consequent on (1) and (2) the essentials of part-singing are grasped through consistent practical experience, and through the steady discipline imposed by a graded course.

(4) This being the case the way is made clear to a great repertoire of unaccompanied vocal music in parts, especially by the great British composers of the age of the madrigal.

(5) When the interplay of separate strands of melody in a musical texture is experienced at first hand the keen pupil will notice how frequent this is in other music, including that for orchestra, to which he may listen, or in the performance of which he may take part.

Individual singers should be encouraged to attempt these pieces as duets. When, however, a class is involved care should be taken to divide it into two groups of equal tonal balance. In both cases preparation is the same. The groups of notes, scales or modes, and the rhythmic structures and patterns should be examined so that the territory covered by each piece is made familiar at once. The teaching notes on p. 4 give such information as may be helpful in this respect. Tempi should be steady, and it is helpful when the teacher conducts. The pupils will learn that the art of corporate music-making depends on an ability to watch the printed music with one eye, the conductor with the other. The singers may, if they wish, also beat the time patterns

Since confidence is to be engendered the tone should not lie below the level of *mezzo-forte*. Sight-reading is the art of going on. Singers should not stop if and when errors occur, but always continue to the end of an exercise. Any mistakes can be sorted out afterwards.

Other relevant points will be found in the prefatory matter of *333 Exercises* and *Bicinia Hungarica*.

Score
MT 875
, K686
1964

Professor Kodály is generous in paying tribute to English choral singing, especially that in the schools. When he refers to this as a national tradition it is not unimportant to realise how old the tradition is. As far back as the twelfth century the people of the northern counties were adept in two-part singing. The famous chronicler Giraldus Cambrensis (which means, Gerald the Welshman) noted this, and, commending their teachers, added that the art was widespread among the children. In the early part of the sixteenth century King Henry VIII maintained one fine choir, Cardinal Wolsey another. Both were celebrated throughout Europe. But Dean Pace, of St. Paul's Cathedral, said that of the two choirs Wolsey's was the better because its members were better sight-readers. True, he was a friend of the Cardinal; but he had a point. It is from this point that the succeeding pieces start.

P. M. Y.

Notes on the Exercises

Each exercise is to be sung in the first place to the solfa syllables, in accordance with the general principles of the *Choral Method*. In each case the tonic, or key-note, is indicated for both voices at the beginning of the stave. Thereafter a chromatic note occurring in a melody is shown to the appropriate syllable on its first appearance. The end of a phrase, or a suitable breathing-place, is marked by a comma. Although there are no dynamic markings the singing should not be without dynamic interest: in this respect the singers, or the teacher, should exercise their own judgment, taking into account the general character of each item and the evident contrasts between different pieces.

It has been suggested elsewhere that the works of Kodály contained in this series are not only adaptable for instruments but also invaluable aids to composition. The following pieces may especially be welcomed as ideal examples for the student of counterpoint.

It will be noted that the variety of the music depends on a wide rhythmic range, the overlapping of phrases, the effective use of discord, the careful introduction of chromatic notes, the skilful disposal of suspensions, and on melodic inversion. In addition to free contrapuntal writing there are various forms of canon, including some by inversion, and even fugues. It will be seen how in every movement the germinal material is extended and developed with singular imagination, but also economy (see, for example, **54**).

The general method is that which developed in the first great phase of choral musical invention, during the period of the Renaissance. But Kodály emphasises that the principles of musical statement for this medium then abstracted are fundamental to all music for voices. By studying the structure of these compositions the singer as well as the would-be composer is helped, for appreciation of the details of melodic behaviour lead to a respect for the part other than the one immediately occupying the singer. It can be seen how the two voices complement each other, and, in due course, "what the music is about".

1 This, like the four exercises following, is based on the pentatonic group familiar through the melodies of earlier books in the series.

2 Voice I: compare bars 1-8 and 9-16, the latter clearly deriving from, and varying the former.

3 Imitation at the interval of the fifth. In bar 4 note the off-beat entry which is to be found subsequently at numerous points. This entry introduces a *suspension*. This is a consonant note sustained over (or under) a change in the other part(s) to become a discord (more rarely another concord) which then, by falling, reaches a (concordant) *resolution*. This device is to be found in all contrapuntal music; especially that of the sixteenth century and that of Bach. Cf. particularly **14, 15, 21, 22, 23, 28, 30, 37, 54, 61, 62.**

4 The note pattern of the first bar will be found frequently in inverted form (i.e. 'upside-down'). Voice II begins in exact imitation at the distance of an octave. (The favourite intervals for vocal imitation are the octave, the fifth, and the fourth).

5 Note imitation by inversion.

6 Voice I builds upwards—*r m*; Voice II pushes away in the opposite direction— *d t₁ l₁ s₁*. During rests the movement of the active voice should be carefully followed (it may at first be hummed until the capacity for silently sensing its direction is acquired) to aid accurate entry. In more extended music the sounds of another part will often help the resting singer to "find the right note".

7, 8 While the upper voice in each case is allocated *r* and *m* (as in **6**) the lower voice explores the complete octave.

9 Two five-note groups: Voice I: *r m f s l*
　　　　　　　　　　　　Voice II: *m r d l₁ s₁*

10 Dorian Mode (see *Bicinia Hungarica II*, **80**), but with a cadence in Voice II as in the key of D minor. Each voice now ranges over an octave (Voice II in fact uses nine notes).

11 Phrygian Mode (see *Bicinia Hungarica III*, **114**).

12 A characteristic "Hungarian" rhythm (cf. **59**). Care is needed with the final interval (minor sixth) in Voice II.

13 Intervals of 4ths and 5ths (Voice I) and 3rds and 4ths (Voice II).

14a, 14b Octave leaps are featured. These are further developed in **14b,** in which the interval of the 7th is also prominent. In this exercise there are also chromatic notes to be considered. In respect of these the singer should carefully note where there are *tones* and *semitones* (c.f. **58**).

16 Voice I, diminished 5th in bar 3.

18 In 2/2 time (as **22, 25, 29, 30, 39, 40, 45, 46, 51, 55, 62, 64**). The minim is the pulse-note, thus 2/2 is not the same as 4/4.

19 Dorian Mode, with B flat introduced (cf. **10**).

23 Voice II, bars 7-8, should note the relationship between *lah-soh* (tone) and *re-de* (tone).

24 In bars 1-4 the parts play into and out of each other. Follow the dotted lines to see how the one voice helps the other.

25 This is in fugal style. The head of the main theme (*subject*) is indicated by a square bracket. It will be seen that when the subject has been sung by the one voice in the tonic key it is then stated by the other in the dominant. This re-statement is called the *answer*. The subject reappears at different pitches (in different keys) throughout a fugue. In bar 5 a contrasting figure, shown by a dotted bracket, emerges. This is the *counter-subject*. This may subsequently appear either above or below the subject. Composers sometimes make considerable use of the counter-subject (as Kodály does here) during the course of a fugue. Sometimes, however, they use it more sparingly (cf. **29, 40, 60, 63,** and **65**, for further examples of fugal writing). In bars 25-26 the 2 voices are in canon. Since they draw the two statements of the melody close together—Voice II coming only one minim later than Voice I—there is a *stretto*.

27 Where the same note appears twice, on adjacent quavers, the second should be slightly accented.

32 Note the variation of accent.

34, 35, 36 Canons by inversion.

37 In bars 22-23 note the crossing of the parts.

38 Dorian Mode (cf. **10** and **19**). The parts are interdependent (cf. **24**).

41 The changes of time signature help to give flexibility (see *333 Elementary Exercises*, **331**, *Bicinia Hungarica I*, **34, 35, 36**).

47 Dorian Mode (cf. **10, 19, 38**).

48, 55, 57 Canon, with Voice II entry a 5th lower.

51 Canon, with Voice II entry a 7th lower.

53 The slurs were added in this exercise only by Kodály.

61 Voice II, bars 25-31, a chromatic scale apart from a missing final semitone, which turns up, however, in bar 35.

62, 64 These related pieces are characterised by series of suspensions.

66 A study in triplets, and with the placing of 3-note against 2-note groups.

66 TWO-PART EXERCISES

ZOLTÁN KODÁLY

Copyright 1963 by Zenemukiado Vallalat, Budapest
Copyright assigned 1964 to Boosey & Hawkes Music Publishers Ltd. for all countries except Hungary, Roumania, Czechoslovakia, Poland, Bulgaria, the German People's Republic and Albania.
English edition © 1964 by Boosey & Hawkes Music Publishers Ltd.   B. & H. 19253   All rights reserved
Printed in England

8

18

34

38

A00001286281B

University of Tulsa
McFarlin Library
Tulsa, Oklahoma